Clever Lateral Thinking Puzzles

Edward J. Harshman
Illustrated by Myron Miller

Sterling Publishing Co., Inc.
New York

For the puzzles following, inspirations are credited to: "Caught in the Act," adapted from "Those Were the Days" by Edward R. Hewitt, Duell, Sloan and Pearce, 1943; "Secret Fuel," adapted from "Sweet Revenge" by George Hayduke, Paladin Press, 1989; "Magazine Subscriptions," adapted from "Steal This Book" by Abbie Hoffman, Pirate Editions, 1971; "Appendicitis," adapted from "I Wish I'd Said That!" by Art Linkletter, Doubleday, 1968; "Miracle Cures," adapted from "Encyclopedia of Jewish Humor" by Henry Spalding, Jonathan David Publishers, 1969; "Happy with the TV Ad," adapted from "Hardcore Hayduke" by George Hayduke, Paladin Press, 1993.

Library of Congress Cataloging-in-Publication Data
Harshman, Edward J.
Clever lateral thinking puzzles / Edward J. Harshman; illustrated by Myron Miller.
p. cm.
Includes index.
ISBN 0-8069-9938-1
1. Puzzles. 2. Lateral thinking. I. Title.
GV1507.L37H35 1997 97-25082
793.73–dc21 CIP

10 9 8 7 6 5 4 3 2 1

Published by Sterling Publishing Company, Inc.
387 Park Avenue South, New York, N.Y. 10016

Distributed in Canada by Sterling Publishing
℅ Canadian Manda Group, One Atlantic Avenue, Suite 105
Toronto, Ontario, Canada M6K 3E7
Distributed in Great Britain and Europe by Cassell PLC
Wellington House, 125 Strand, London WC2R 0BB, England
Distributed in Australia by Capricorn Link (Australia) Pty Ltd.
P.O. Box 6651, Baulkham Hills, Business Centre,
NSW 2153, Australia
Manufactured in the United States of America

Sterling ISBN 0-8069-9938-1

CONTENTS

PUZZLES

Batty Banditry

Welcome, Slasher

Bob, a fifteen-year-old boy with a record of violent crimes, approached a screened porch. Taking out a switchblade, he cut through every screen panel with large diagonal rips. A police officer drove by in a patrol car, saw what the boy was doing, and was pleased. Explain.

Clues: 41 /Answer: 75.

Smashed Taillights

Later, Bob picked up a tire wrench and smashed the taillights of a car that he had never seen before. Police officers witnessed his act and arrested not him, but the owner of the car. Explain.

Clues: 41 /Answer: 76.

Supposed to Kill?

A man drew a gun, pointed it at another man who was known to be totally law-abiding, and pulled the trigger. Click! The gun wasn't loaded. Everyone present, which included at least ten people, was surprised and outraged. Why was the intended victim blamed for the incident?

Clues: 41–42 /Answer: 78.

Burning Down the Building

An old apartment building caught fire. Most apartments were damaged badly, and many people were left homeless. An investigator arrived from the fire department. A shady man pulled him aside into a dark corner of the building and handed him five hundred-dollar bills. "It would be better for both of us," said the shady man, "if something went wrong with the investigation. Lose the papers, or whatever." The investigator looked at the money and protested, "But the landlord will want to file an insurance claim and need our report." "He won't mind," the shady man replied. "Be nice to other fire victims and don't ask questions." The investigator pocketed the money and conveniently forgot the case. Why did the landlord not get upset?

Clues: 42 /Answer: 80.

Caught in the Act

A woman walked into a police station. "I want to report a pickpocket," she announced. A man staggered in behind her, his hand in her coat pocket. "Arrest that man!" she continued, pointing to him. He was arrested, tried, and convicted of picking pockets. Why did he enter the police station in a posture that obviously suggested his crime?

Clues: 42 /Answer: 82.

Slippery Sidney Slipped Up

Slippery Sidney rented a car for a month. He returned it and paid the rental fee. Three months later, he was arrested for attempting to defraud the rental-car company. What happened?

Clues: 42–43 /Answer: 84.

Honest Ivan

The rental-car company, after convicting Sidney, advised all personnel to watch for odometer tampering. Later, Ivan rented a car in central Florida. Two days later, it was badly damaged when a truck lost control and hit it on a thruway in Virginia. The odometer reading was too low to account for the trip from Florida to Virginia, but Ivan easily went free. How?

Clues: 43 /Answer: 86.

Robbing the Bank

Upon being tipped off that a large organization paid its employees on a certain day, and that its employees went to a specific bank to cash their paychecks at a certain time on that day, a gang decided to rob the bank at exactly that day and time. They would have been better off if they had robbed the bank on any other day than that one or at any other time during that day. Why?

Clues: 43 /Answer: 88.

He Called the Police

A burglar broke into a house, intending to steal from it. While still in the house, he called the police. Why?

Clues: 43 /Answer: 90.

Arrested Anyway

Rocky Redneck carried a gun. He had a state-issued firearm permit that allowed him to do so, and he was careful to obey the law. One day, he went to visit his relatives across the country, in another state. Rocky had a firearm permit from that state, too; and he could legally carry his gun there. He found out from the airlines that he could take his gun with him if it was declared to the airline staff and was in checked baggage. Ever the law-abiding citizen, Rocky packed the gun in a suitcase, told the airline clerk about it, and had the suitcase checked. So why was Rocky arrested for weapons possession?

Clues: 44 /Answer: 92.

No Ransom Demand

A man entered a government building and went through a weapons-detector search. Then he entered a government office and displayed a sawed-off shotgun. "Up against the wall, everyone!" he ordered. Then, after everyone complied, he called the police. When police officers arrived, he put down his gun and cooperated with them. He refused to defend himself in court and was convicted of assault with a deadly weapon and given a long prison sentence. "What's the point of taking people hostage if you don't make a ransom demand?" asked a news reporter. "I thought of making one," he replied, "but there just didn't seem to be any point to it." So why did the man act as he did?

Clues: 44 /Answer: 76.

Escaping the Kidnappers

Brenda had been kidnapped. She was locked in a room and placed on the floor, hands tied behind her back. She knew where she was, but had no chance of escape. Or did she? A telephone was on a table. She waited until no one was nearby, then she pulled the telephone to the floor. Alas! A dial lock! What did she do?

Clues: 44 /Answer: 78.

People Puzzles

Hearing Them Quickly

"Hey, Pop! Can I have some money?" asked Dana. "The Electric Earsplitters are giving a concert here in town next week, and I really want to hear it." His father put down the television listings, turned off the TV, and firmly declined. "But that's my favorite group!" protested Dana. "I want to buy tickets real fast so I can hear them perform as soon as possible." "If that's what's most important to you," replied his father, "then you won't need any tickets." Explain.

Clues: 45 /Answer: 80.

Motorcycle Madness

Together, Peter and his brother Jamie owned some land in the country. They enjoyed outdoor activities on it, but lately had had trouble with motorcyclists who ignored the fences and no-trespassing signs and noisily rode where they wished. One day, Jamie and his wife Amy were outside, peacefully eating a picnic lunch, when two people on a motorcycle cut through the grass and raced past them. Jamie jumped up and ran to his car to chase them, when Peter drove up in his jeep. "They went that way!" shouted Jamie, pointing. Peter gunned the motor in hot pursuit. "Did you catch them?" Amy asked them later. "No," replied Peter. "They slipped through a gap in the fence and escaped." Why was Amy pleased?

Clues: 45 /Answer: 82.

A Crying Problem

Sandra had problems with her husband and was on strained terms with his parents. Nevertheless, one day she called them and chatted for about fifteen minutes. They thanked her for calling and told her that they felt better about her after talking. When she hung up the telephone, she burst into tears. Explain.

Clues: 45 /Answer: 84.

She Never Fixed Him Up

When Mitch started working in the small office, he was noted for his shyness. Anna, a co-worker, found out about his recent divorce and offered to set up a blind date for him. Eager to establish a new social life, he accepted her offer. But she never followed up on it, and he never met anyone else. Why did Mitch not mind?

Clues: 46 /Answer: 86.

Happy That She Cursed Him

A man called the woman he loved, and she cursed at him and hung up angrily. Why was he happy?

Clues: 46 /Answer: 88.

Evicted

A man locked his son out of the house. The son thanked him. Explain.

Clues: 46 /Answer: 75.

Crazy Cars and Tricky Transport

Driving the Wrong Car

Hermie the Hermit had a car that needed repair but was still drivable. He had another car that worked. He drove the first car to a repair shop. To avoid asking someone else to drive him home, he had fastened his two cars together and towed one with the other. He therefore arrived at the repair shop with two cars instead of one and could easily drive away with the working car. But why did he tow the working car with the broken one, and not the other way around?

Clues: 47 /Answer: 90.

Safe Smash-Up

A car slowly started to move forward. Then it picked up speed. Faster and faster it went, until it crashed through a guardrail and went over a cliff. It fell over a hundred feet and was badly damaged. No one was killed or injured. In fact, no one was even afraid of being killed or injured. Why not?

Clues: 47 /Answer: 92.

Contagious Carsickness?

Stan and Jan were driving along a highway. Fran, a small child strapped into the back seat, said "I feel sick." "It's probably carsickness," replied Jan. "We'll be stopping soon," said Stan, "then you can get out for some fresh air." Less than ten minutes later, Stan shut off the engine and they all got out of the car. But within half an hour, Jan complained: "Fran has motion sickness, and I do, too." Jan did not normally get carsick. What was happening?

Clues: 47 /Answer: 76.

What Drained the Battery?

Walter forgot to allow for the slowness of traffic in the rain and was late for work. He hurriedly drove into the parking lot, parked, turned off the windshield wipers, jumped out of his car, slammed the door, and ran for the main entrance. That evening, he could not get the car started. The battery was dead. He got a jump start from a co-worker, drove home, and used his battery recharger to put a good charge on the battery. But despite careful testing, he never found out why the battery went dead. Can you?

Clues: 48 /Answer: 75.

Seasonal Mileage

Claude gets noticeably better mileage while driving the last mile to or from work than he does during any other part of the trip in summer. But not in winter. Why not?

Clues: 48 /Answer: 78.

She Arrived On Time

Daryl and Carol had arranged to meet at a coffee house but something came up. Daryl looked in the phone book, found Carol's home phone number and called her. "I know we were supposed to meet in the coffee house in two hours, but my boss called and I have to reschedule. I'm due at the office two hours from now." "That's too bad," replied Carol, "but I can meet you at the coffee house in two minutes if you'd like." Daryl agreed and, because he lived right across the street from it, was there in two minutes. He was content to wait. but Carol was waiting for him. "You live clear across town," noted Daryl. "How could you get here so fast?"

Clues: 49 /Answer: 80.

A Token Wait in a Token Line

Smart Stephanie worked in a city and took the subway to work every morning during rush hour. In the evening, also during rush hour, she took the subway home again. To use the subway, she had to put a subway token into a turnstile as she entered the station from the street. Although she was one of numerous commuters at those hours and had to stand in crowded subway cars, she never had to wait in a long line to buy tokens. Why not?

Clues: 49 /Answer: 82.

The Late Train

Amanda got onto a train. After traveling about one thousand miles, she got off. She arrived at her destination forty-five minutes late. There had been no delays, and the train had picked her up on time. Why was it late?

Clues: 49 /Answer: 84.

Odd Offices

Stubborn Steve

Steve went to an office supply store and got a ream (500 sheets) of standard-size paper. "We have a special today," a sales clerk told Steve helpfully as he carried the ream to the checkout counter. "It's a better grade of paper than what you're carrying, and it's cheaper, too." Steve investigated and he discovered that the paper on sale was the same size, same color, and of a heavier weight than the paper he had in his hand. Used in certain printers or copiers, it would be less likely to jam than would the paper Steve had chosen. And sure enough, it was much less expensive. Why, therefore, did Steve decline the paper on sale and retain his original choice?

Clues: 50 /Answer: 86.

Making the Grade

Nervous Nell, a college student with a straight-A average, went into her professor's office. She told the receptionist she was worried about her grade on the final paper for her course. "I want to be sure I pass this course," said Nell. "Is there some way I can be notified of my final grade as soon as possible?" The receptionist, sympathetic to her concern, replied, "If you hand in a self-addressed stamped postcard with your term paper, the professor will write the grade for the paper and the course on it and mail it to you as soon as the paper is graded. That's much faster than waiting for a transcript." "Oh," said Nell, "but I don't think I can do that." Why not?

Clues: 50 /Answer: 88.

Spaced-Out at the Computer

A secretary was working at her computer. She had a chart loaded into her word-processing program and had to rearrange it. The hard part of her job was removing extra spaces. The word-processing program had a "replace" command. She could replace any sequence of characters with any other sequence, or with nothing at all. So how could she replace many spaces in a row with only one space? This is not the same as replacing all spaces with nothing, because then there wouldn't be the one space that she wanted.

Clues: 50–51 /Answer: 90.

The Fast Elevator Trip

Bill was nearly late for an appointment in a tall office building. He ran into the building, reached the elevators that led to the correct range of floors, pressed the button, and waited. After a tense few minutes, an elevator arrived and opened its doors to receive passengers. Why didn't he get on?

Clues: 51 /Answer: 92.

The Nonstop Elevator Trip

Bill got to his appointment on time. "I was worried about those elevators for a minute," said Bill, "but I figured out a way to get here faster." Then he explained his reasoning. "Never thought of that," said Jill, who worked there and greeted him, "but if you just get in an elevator, it sure can take a long time. I have a way to beat the system, too." "What's your way?" he asked. "I just get in, and when the elevator first stops, I get out," she replied. He couldn't figure out how that strategy would save any time. Can you?

Clues: 51 /Answer: 77.

Too Precise

Mary and Jerry were working in an office. Jerry was writing something, and Mary looked over his shoulder. "That's too precise," complained Mary. "It should be more vague, harder to understand." "That's crazy!" replied Jerry. "The entire philosophy of the business we are in is based on that kind of reasoning I know, but that's not being tolerated here!" "Yes, precision is our great strength," admitted Mary, "and ordinarily I'd agree with you. But in this particular instance, no." Where were they?

Clues: 51–52 /Answer: 78.

Exceptionally Vague

Mary heard Jerry out, explaining what he was writing, and easily agreed that it should be deliberately misleading. What was he writing?

Clues: 52 /Answer: 80.

The Hostile Voter

Charlie received a telephone call from the office of a local politician. A fast-talking campaign volunteer explained the benefits of the candidate, including a lecture on his platform. Charlie asked if the volunteer was calling at the request of the candidate, heard the volunteer's answer, and announced firmly that he intended to vote for the candidate's opponent. Then he hung up. Explain.

Clues: 52 /Answer: 82.

A Mystery Fax

When his private phone line rang and he picked it up, the business executive heard a loud, squealing noise. Why did he receive a fax call on his private line, a phone that was known not to have a fax machine connected to it?

Clues: 52 /Answer: 84.

Another Mystery Fax

One of the executive's subordinates sent a fax to a colleague. The subordinate would have preferred to have merely called the colleague in an ordinary way, but instead handwrote a note and faxed it. Why?

Clues: 53 /Answer: 86.

Problems with Personnel

Raymond, a business executive in a large company, needed a department head. After placing a classified ad, he reviewed the responses sent on to him from the personnel department. When a colleague mentioned a potentially suitable friend of hers who was looking for work, Raymond tracked him down, interviewed him, checked references, and hired him. Then he complained vigorously to the personnel department. Why?

Clues: 53 /Answer: 88.

More Problems with Personnel

It's true that all the references checked out positively, and the interviewee was hired. But a few weeks later, the colleague who recommended him to Raymond showed up—and the newly hired department head was fired on the spot. Explain.

Clues: 53 /Answer: 90.

Dismaying Dizziness

Raymond finally got an honest department head and had her office redecorated, installing new wallpaper, a refinished desk, and a bright ceiling lamp. He had received complaints that that office was dark and dirty, and he had no wish to alienate a new employee without cause. Unfortunately, she complained of dizziness in her office. He entered it to investigate, and he got dizzy too. Neither of them was dizzy anywhere else. What was the problem?

Clues: 54 /Answer: 75.

Asinine Actions

Giving Wayne the Boot

Wayne was asleep when a boot crashed through his bedroom window, waking him up. Loud music came from the house next door, further irritating him. He jumped up, shook his fist at his neighbor's house, and shouted some obscenities toward it. "It's three A.M.," he yelled truthfully. "If you don't turn down that racket *now*, I'm calling the cops!" The music persisted and Wayne did as he had threatened and called the police. When they arrived, the officers refused to prosecute for the noise, even though it was obviously excessively loud. After the police officers explained the facts to Wayne, he was happy to forgive not only the noise but also the broken window. Explain.

Clues: 54 /Answer: 77.

Racing the Drawbridge

Park Street included a drawbridge over a river. As its warning lights flashed, Clarence proceeded toward the bridge. The barriers were lowered, blocking the road. Clarence ignored them. The drawbridge itself opened, and Clarence gunned the motor and aimed right at it. But there was no collision. Why not?

Clues: 54 /Answer: 78.

Recycled Salt

Can salt be recycled? How?

Clues: 55 /Answer: 80.

Scared of Her Shadow?

Wacky Wendy, who lives in Florida, finds it particularly important, when she is driving and sees the shadow of her car, to roll down her window. Why?

Clues: 55 /Answer: 82.

Picture the Tourists

"I have a manual focus camera," said Sherman Shutterbug to his friend Sal as they sat next to each other on a tour bus. "Mine is autofocus," replied Sal. "It's much quicker, because the camera measures the distance to whatever I'm photographing and focuses automatically." "Then I think we'd better change places," said Sherman. Why?

Clues: 55 /Answer: 84.

The Mirror

A mirror is mounted over the headboard of a bed. It is there because someone has a bad back. Explain.

Clues: 55–56 /Answer: 86.

The Empty Wrapper

A woman was at the checkout lane of a supermarket. She removed several items from her cart and put them on the conveyor belt that led to the cashier. The cashier noted their prices and passed the items along to be bagged. A perfectly ordinary process, but one of the items entered and passed along was an empty wrapper. The cashier realized that the wrapper was empty, but charged for it anyway. Why?

Clues: 56 /Answer: 88.

Secret Fuel

Marvin often sneaked into his neighbor's driveway in the middle of the night in the course of playing a prank. He would quietly unscrew the fuel cap from his neighbor's car and pour gasoline into its fuel tank. What was he up to?

Clues: 56 /Answer: 92.

Forgot to Stop?

Angus was driving along a road at about thirty miles per hour. Suddenly, he jumped out of his car. He had not applied the brakes, and the car was still moving. He was not a stunt man for a movie or otherwise involved in deliberately risky activity. What happened?

Clues: 56–57 /Answer: 84.

Short-Lived Messages

Yolanda regularly writes and destroys messages to herself. Usually, people write such notes as reminders, such as in calendars. But Yolanda never expects to forget what was in the messages. Why write them?

Clues: 57 /Answer: 78.

More Short-Lived Writing

Yolanda often passes a writing instrument across a surface for which it is intended and, within a few seconds, erases the result. What is she doing?

Clues: 58 /Answer: 81.

Haphazard Happenings

The Mail Is In!

One day earlier, little Oscar had mailed an order form for a wanted toy. Now, he was constantly pestering his mother to let him check the mail. Suddenly, looking out the window at the apartment complex mailboxes, he shouted, "The mail is in! The mail is in!" Neither he nor his mother had seen a mail carrier, mail truck, or any activity near the mailboxes, but Oscar was right, it was in. How had he known?

Clues: 58 /Answer: 77.

Magazine Subscriptions

Magazines often contain postcards meant for use by new subscribers. Some people consider them a nuisance and just toss them out. Some don't, even though they won't ever use them for their intended purpose. Why not throw them away?

Clues: 58–59 /Answer: 82.

Soliciting in Seattle

Two friends, who lived in different well-to-do neighborhoods in Seattle, were conversing. "Almost every week, I get a few people who knock on my door and ask for money," said one. "Odd. That rarely happens to me," replied the other. But there is a good explanation for the difference. What is it?

Clues: 59 /Answer: 86.

It's a Dog's Life

Fred and Jed saw a badly injured puppy. It had been hit by a car, and its left eye and part of its left front leg were missing. Fortunately, it had received competent treatment. A bandage covered what remained of its left front leg, and a patch was fastened over the left half of its face. Fred picked up the puppy and stroked it gently. It whimpered weakly as he put it down. "Poor thing," said Jed. "Look what it's been through." Fred nodded his head grimly. "I know. But it will almost certainly be alive in a year. That healthy-looking dog over there won't," he added, pointing to a frisky dog that wagged its tail eagerly. What was Fred's reasoning?

Clues: 59 /Answer: 88.

Not from the USA

Belinda Blabbermouth told a riddle. "I am standing in a place where I can travel north, south, east, or west, and soon be in the USA. Where am I?" After everyone gave up, she laughed, "The USA, of course!" After a few seconds, someone else spoke up: "Not necessarily. The country I come from, for example." Where was he from?

Clues: 59–60 /Answer: 89.

Dots on the I's

"The teacher marked you wro-ong," Jimmy sang out teasingly during school recess. "You didn't put dots on all your I's!" "Is that so!" countered Timmy. "Betcha don't know how to draw a small I with a dot on it!" he challenged. Jimmy did so, and Timmy looked defeated. A few moments later, Timmy retorted, "Well, now I have dots over my I's and *you* don't!" One glance at Timmy and Jimmy burst out laughing. So did Timmy. Half the class did, too. Explain.

Clues: 60 /Answer: 83.

Power Failure

While Horace slept peacefully, a transformer on the street burned out and stopped all electrical power to his house. The power was restored two hours later, while Horace was still asleep. He awoke the next morning and noted with annoyance that all of his digital clocks were blinking and needed to be reset. "I hate power failures," he grumbled, as he carried his battery-powered watch to the VCR, the microwave oven, and other devices that needed to have their clocks reset. But Horace had no idea that the power had failed during the night, much less how long. Explain.

Clues: 60 /Answer: 92.

Afraid of the Country

"The city is so hot and sticky during the summer," Willie said to his friend Nicolai. "I've got a house in the country. Can you join me there next weekend?" Nicolai smiled. "Ah, the country. Like a farm?" "Yes, you could say that," continued Willie. "It used to be a farm a long time ago." "That's good," continued Nicolai. "When I was a boy in Russia, I lived on a farm. There were cows and pigs, and they were like my friends. It will be good to go away from this hot city and be on a farm again." "You'll like it. It's so peaceful there," said Willie, continuing. "Nice and quiet. No cars. Not even animals." Nicolai suddenly stiffened, and stared straight ahead hardly breathing for close to a minute. "No," he eventually whispered quietly, "I cannot. Thank you for your lovely offer. I would like to, but cannot go." Why was Nicolai terrified at the thought of Willie's country house?

Clues: 60 /Answer: 77.

Long-Life Bulbs

Eccentric Eric flipped an ordinary light switch in his living room. The lights went on, apparently in an ordinary way. But there was special hidden circuitry involved. He was right when he boasted, "My lights are wired so that the bulbs last much longer than average. I rarely have to change them." Explain.

Clues: 61 /Answer: 81.

They Had a Ball

Two men stood on a softball field and practiced throwing and catching just before a game. "Over here! Over here!" shouted Ned, slapping his fist into his mitt. Ted threw the softball to him. "Good catch! Throw me a grounder!" shouted Ted. Ned returned the ball by throwing it along the ground, as requested. "Now a high one! Right here! Right here!" Ted threw the ball high in the air—and Ned ran about ten feet to his left, reached up, and caught the ball easily. "Good arm, but your aim is a little crooked," he announced. "No it isn't," replied Ted." "So what's wrong with throwing the high ball right to where I was standing?" retorted Ned. What indeed?

Clues: 61 /Answer: 83.

Ballpark Befuddlement

Nine men stood together at the edge of a field. One of them watched a ball intently and swung at it. Missed! He took another swing. Whack! The ball sailed up and to the left. A third swing. Zoom! This ball soared up and directly forward, and the man was pleased. Why didn't anyone run to retrieve the third ball?

Clues: 61 /Answer: 78.

Crass Creditors and Dull Debtors

Overdue Payment

Jim sent a payment on a debt every month. One month, he accidentally missed the deadline and got a warning. He was eager to pay as quickly as possible and feared that a mailed check might be delayed in the mail, but didn't want to pay extra for registered mail, overnight delivery, or anything else. How did he minimize the chance of a delayed payment?

Clues: 62 /Answer: 85.

Wrong Order

Jim waited. Sure enough, he got a message that the payment had arrived as he expected. Then he got a telephone call from his creditor, who had a secretary with an unusual attention to detail. "You sent next month's payment, too," said the secretary. "I figured that the check with the higher number would be for next month, and the one with the lower number was for this month. But the higher-number check got here first." "It's up to you," replied Jim, who didn't really care as long as the payment had arrived. "But although I wrote the other one first and mailed it first, I'm not surprised that it arrived later." Why?

Clues: 62 /Answer: 87.

I've Got Your Number

Kingfist, a bookie well known for aggressive collection practices, was pursuing Sam Skiptown, who owed him money. From a distance, he spotted Sam and quietly followed him to his house. The house was well guarded, with a burglar alarm system and a climbable but inconvenient fence. Kingfist made plans. Within a week, he called Sam and warned him: "Pay now, or take the consequences." Sam was horrified. "How did you get my number?" he asked. "No questions," ordered Kingfist. "Let's just say I went to a lot of trouble to ask you nicely." Sam never figured out how Kingfist learned his telephone number, which was unpublished and known to only a few trusted friends. Can you?

Clues: 62 /Answer: 89.

Collecting Backwards

Kingfist forced a debtor to write him a check. Then he took it to the bank to cash it. Why did he first deposit money in the debtor's account?

Clues: 63 /Answer: 90.

Better Late Than Prompt

Kingfist was engaging in his usual habit of bullying a debtor into paying. "You don't have the cash? I'll tell you what I'm going to do," explained Kingfist. "Sign this contract, and I'll tear up this one you signed earlier." The debtor reviewed the contracts and saw that the old one was his original loan and the new one was for the same amount, but for smaller payments that added up to the same total as the old one. The new one, overall, meant that the debtor didn't have to come up with money as fast and actually had a lower interest rate. And the new contract had no penalties for late payment, including harassment rights, that were not in the old contract either. The debtor was happy to sign. "Thanks!" replied Kingfist. "I'll be seeing you!" And that's exactly what happened. Kingfist was delighted, and the debtor soon realized he had blundered by signing the new contract. Explain.

Clues: 63 /Answer: 93.

The Debtor Paid

Kingfist had trouble with another debtor. "What can you do about it?" was the debtor's attitude. "The collection hassle is more than the bad debt is worth, and we both know it." But within two months, the customer paid the loan in full. Why?

Clues: 63 /Answer: 79.

Daffy Doctoring

She Was in the Hospital

Alan called the office where his wife worked. “I’m sorry,” came the reply. “There was a bad accident on the highway a few minutes ago, and she’s expected to be in the operating room for at least six hours.” “That’s too bad,” he replied. “Can you ask her to call me when she gets out?” Sure enough, about six hours later, Alan heard from his wife. Why was she not upset that Alan didn’t visit her personally?

Clues: 64 /Answer: 81.

Appendicitis

Zeke and his wife lived in a rural area. One evening, his wife felt ill. Zeke called the local physician. “Doc, I think my wife may have appendicitis,” he explained. “Nonsense! I took out her appendix myself five years ago,” said the doctor. But Zeke’s wife proved to have appendicitis. Explain.

Clues: 64 /Answer: 83.

Crossed Vision

If your eyes are crossed, then you see worse than usual. But if your fingers are crossed, then you may be able to see better than usual. Explain.

Clues: 64 /Answer: 85.

Night Blindness Cure

What two questions can cure some cases of night blindness, without formal eye examinations or blood tests?

Clues: 65 /Answer: 87.

A Sweet Problem

White, refined sugar is frowned on as a dietary supplement and is especially to be avoided by diabetics (other than as an emergency treatment for insulin overdose or similar problems) —except for what?

Clues: 65 /Answer: 89.

Miracle Cures

Some resorts and shrines are known throughout the world for providing effective treatments for conditions believed to be incurable. One explanation is divine intervention, a literal miracle. Another is faith and belief in the cure. A third is an unknown but potentially discoverable scientific explanation, such as an unidentified ingredient in springwater. What is a fourth?

Clues: 65 /Answer: 91.

Not a Trusted Doctor

Cassandra and her boyfriend went to a lecture. At it, a doctor described a reputed cure for senility. "Nonsense!" said Cassandra. "He is no more a doctor than I am." "What do you mean?" asked her boyfriend. "He showed us his medical school diploma." What did she mean?

Clues: 65–66 /Answer: 77.

The Plumber's Pressure

A plumber received a checkup in the doctor's office. "You have high blood pressure," said the doctor, after measuring it with a cuff. "You'll have to watch the salt and take blood-pressure medication." "That makes no sense, Doc," replied the plumber. "Didn't you tell me last visit that I had something else the matter with me?" "Yes, I did," replied the doctor, "and you still do." "That's why I don't trust that pressure gauge of yours," said the plumber. Why was he skeptical?

Clues: 66 /Answer: 87.

Rx Lead Poisoning

A doctor examined a new patient and identified the woman's ailment. Later, as they spoke, he filled in her records, including medical insurance coverage. Suddenly, the doctor said, "In that case, I would suggest you go to an old building and eat some lead paint chips from its walls." Why?

Clues: 66 /Answer: 79.

Long Walk for the Disabled

A man had a serious accident and partially recovered from it. Previously, he was in good physical shape. Now, he was disabled, but not in a way that qualified him for handicapped parking rights. Instead, he often had to park farther from destinations than he did before the accident. Explain.

Clues: 66–67 /Answer: 81.

Eccentric Electronics

Happy with the TV Ad

A man went to a television station and bought one minute's worth of advertising time. He handed a videocassette to the station manager and learned to the second exactly when his one-minute tape would be on the station. Just before the scheduled time, the man turned on his TV set, tuned it to the correct channel, and waited. At exactly the time for his ad, a test pattern came on. The sound, an intense pure tone, did not change for a full minute. The picture stayed the same, too. Then the man, pleased, turned off his TV set. Explain.

Clues: 67 /Answer: 83.

Time for Repairs

Dilton got a new digital watch and put it on his wrist. At work, he looked at the office clock and checked his watch. They showed the same time. Later that morning, he couldn't make sense of what his watch showed and decided to return to the store with it. But before lunchtime, he again noted that his watch showed the correct time. During his lunch break, he returned to the store. But the salesclerk to whom he showed the watch noted that it showed the correct time, and Dilton agreed that it did. Dilton was soon satisfied that he had a watch that worked perfectly. But the clerk neither opened it for repairs nor replaced it. Explain.

Clues: 67 /Answer: 85.

Strange Sounds

Modern movies, unlike those of half a century ago, are often made with picture and sound recorded at different times. Sound-effects technicians watch the picture and make the appropriate sounds, perhaps walking in place on a hard floor to generate the sound of footsteps. How can this method of recording sound be detected in the final movies?

Clues: 67–68 /Answer: 89.

Watching the Game

Elmer had a sports bar, one with several TV screens hooked up to a satellite receiver and tuned to receive popular sports events. One day, there was a ball game in a stadium nearby. The game was blacked out from the local television stations and even from local satellite receivers, but Elmer and his customers saw the game on television anyway. How?

Clues: 68 /Answer: 91.

Digital Downfall

Why do hi-fi enthusiasts sometimes dislike compact disks and other digital recording media?

Clues: 68 /Answer: 94.

The TV Obeyed

Jake had some friends over to watch a popular new movie on his brand-new big-screen TV with state-of-the-art surround-sound speakers. As the credits ended and everyone started to the kitchen for snacks, an obnoxious commercial came on. Jake turned to the set. "Oh, shut up!" he shouted angrily at the TV—and it did! Explain.

Clues: 68–69 /Answer 83.

The VCR Timers

Benny and Jenny were busy hooking up a new videocassette recorder. "I'll never understand these instructions!" shouted Benny, as he tried to set the VCR timer to record his favorite show every other night. "They make no sense to me, either," admitted Jenny. They returned to the store for advice and the salesclerk admitted that the instructions confused him too. "I recommend this for most of my customers," he said, showing them a battery-powered device that looked like a VCR remote control unit. "You can set it to signal start-recording and stop-recording for any time you want, once a week, every day, or whenever." Benny and Jenny looked through its instruction book and understood it easily. "Great!" said Benny. "Now I can tape my favorite show every other night." "No you can't," admitted the salesclerk. "It won't let you do that—just every night or once a week." "Yes we can," replied Jenny. "After a trip to the hardware store, that is." How?

Clues: 69 /Answer: 85.

The VCR Remote Control

After Benny and Jenny set up their VCR to record their show on alternate nights, Benny looked for the remote control to the other VCR in the bedroom. "I put it away so the dog wouldn't get it," explained Jenny. "That's a nuisance," replied Benny. "Then we can't operate the VCR while lying in bed." "Yes we can," replied Jenny. How?

Clues: 69–70 /Answer: 93.

No Television Trouble

Stuart was driving a car along a highway. A small television set sat on the dashboard, and Stuart could see its screen. The theme music from Stuart's favorite television show came on. At a police roadblock set up to screen and catch lawbreakers, a state trooper observed Stuart and his television set, but did not warn or arrest him. Why not?

Clues: 70 /Answer: 91.

Inefficiency Pays Off

A certain mechanical object is often made in several models by each of its manufacturers. Government regulations require that its retail sellers offer information that will allow part of the cost of operation to be calculated. Of a manufacturer, the models of the object offered can be ranked from least to most expensive. The cheapest model costs relatively little to buy and to operate and has simple controls. The most expensive model costs most to operate and generally has the most elaborate controls. But the most expensive model is not necessarily the one that is most effective at doing what it is designed to do. What is the object?

Clues: 70 /Answer: 93.

Mad Money

Worth Twenty Dollars

Nick had a series 1950 $20 bill. Instead of saying "Twenty dollars" at the bottom, it said "Will pay to the bearer on demand twenty dollars." He told his friend Dick, "If I can get twenty dollars' worth of gold or silver, then I may as well exchange this bill at the Federal Reserve office that issued it." Was he right?

Clues: 70–71 /Answer: 81.

Slow-Witted Customers

In northern Florida, fast-food chains often have a pricing policy that works only because many customers do not think carefully. What is it?

Clues: 71 /Answer: 94.

Banking on the Boycott

On the principal street of a small town, a fast-food restaurant chain was planning to open. Local citizens, wary of litter and disruption, and eager to defend the livelihoods of their local diners, planned retaliation. At a town meeting, a woman urged strict enforcement of litter and parking-meter laws. A man stood up and suggested something more devious: that everyone go there and order something, but insist on a special order (no lettuce with the hamburger, etc.) so as to overwhelm the help. Another man, who happened to work at the town bank, approved of the action, but recommended that they all come to his place of business first. Why?

Clues: 71 /Answer: 91.

Old Money But Good Money

What two changes affected U.S. currency in 1968 that, if considered together, scare certain conservatives?

Clues: 71–72 /Answer: 83.

Secret Business

Two men were on the telephone, discussing a multi-million-dollar business deal. They used electronic scramblers, so that no one could easily listen in on their conversation. They also each had much more sophisticated scramblers, which were harder to obtain and which encoded conversations more securely than the scramblers that they used. Why did they use the less secure scramblers?

Clues: 72 /Answer: 93.

Gas-Station Glitch

During a fuel shortage, George drove to a gas station and waited in line behind many other motorists. A man in the familiar gas-station uniform walked over and explained to him, "We have a ten-dollar limit. To save time, we are taking cash only and collecting payment in advance." George gave the man a ten-dollar bill. When he reached the front of the line and parked in front of a pump, he asked for his ten dollars' worth of gas. "The limit is five dollars," replied the attendant. What happened?

Clues: 72 /Answer: 94.

Marketing Muddle

What carelessly marketed name of a car may provoke concerns about auto safety?

Clues: 72–73 /Answer: 91.

Easy Money

The television set had a retail value of $100. Butch worked at the wholesale warehouse and said that stores bought them for $60 each. The warehouse bought them in large lots for $45 apiece. He offered to sell you all you want for $30 each. If they cost $45, then how could he make a profit at $30?

***Clues:** 73 /**Answer:** 77.*

Too Much Money

An investor was reading the description of a proposed investment. It was a limited partnership, so that the investor would have no control over the management of the investment. But there were safeguards in place so that if the person who managed the investment made a profit, then the investor would too. Suddenly, the investor discovered something that made him decide not to invest. "Too much money," he muttered to himself, throwing the description onto his desk. Too little money invested in a company can be a bad sign, for it may go bankrupt. But why would the investor be afraid of too much money?

***Clues:** 73 /**Answer:** 79.*

Goofy Gambling

Lottery Logic

Many states run lotteries as a way to raise money. For every dollar received from lottery-ticket sales, perhaps half a dollar is paid out to winners. Therefore, the weighted-average value of the expected winnings of a one-dollar ticket is perhaps half a dollar. Therefore, although a lottery ticket may be a fun expense because it carries a chance to get rich, it is never a good investment from a financial-planning perspective. Right?

Clues: 73–74 /Answer: 89.

Youthful Gamble

Some people gamble irrationally and are at risk of losing more money than they can afford to. Laws exist, therefore, to prohibit gambling except under special circumstances. It would seem especially important to keep young adults from gambling, for bad habits can be formed while young that cannot be easily corrected later. But certain young adults are allowed to gamble, in that they pay money and receive something of greater or lesser value, in exchange for that money, that is partially determined by chance. Explain.

Clues: 74 /Answer: 79.

Staged Roulette

Police officers, their spouses, and their families put together a talent show to raise money for their retirement fund. One of the events at the show was a skit about the evils of gambling. In one scene, a misguided man lost most of his money to a crooked roulette-wheel operator. It was learned too late that the audience could see the stage from above and would observe the number into which a roulette ball would drop. What did the producers do?

Clues: 74 /Answer: 87.

CLUES

Batty Banditry

Welcome, Slasher

Q: Were the boy and the policeman what they appeared to be and not, for example, actors for a movie?

A: Yes.

Q: Was the policeman honest?

A: Yes.

Q: Did the boy act in retaliation, perhaps to deter a criminal who could not be prosecuted by normal methods?

A: No.

Smashed Taillights

Q: Did the owner give Bob permission to smash the taillights?

A: No.

Q: Had the car been stolen?

A: No.

Q: After the taillights were smashed, was something important revealed behind them?

A: Yes.

Supposed to Kill?

Q: Did the intended victim run or call for help?

A: No.

Q: Having learned that the gun was not loaded, did anyone try to grab it or otherwise forcibly intervene?

A: No.

Q: The incident did not result in death or serious injury. Did anyone want it to?

A: No.

Burning Down the Building

Q: Did anyone bribe the landlord?

A: No.

Q: Did the fire destroy evidence of a crime?

A: No.

Q: Did a tenant set the fire, perhaps out of anger?

A: No.

Caught in the Act

Q: Was he really a pickpocket?

A: Yes.

Q: Did he want to be arrested?

A: No.

Q: Did he act rationally?

A: Yes.

Slippery Sidney Slipped Up

Q: Had Sidney tried to sell the rented car by forging a title to it?

A: No.

Q: Did Sidney return the car intact and drivable, with no collision damage and no replacement of good major parts with inferior ones?

A: Yes.

Q: Was the fraud obvious to the rental-car company, but only after at least a month had passed?

A: Yes.

Honest Ivan

Q: Had Ivan wanted to use the car for at least two months, including driving back to Florida for a vacation with his family?

A: Yes.

Q: Did Ivan cause the collision that damaged the car or contribute to it in any way?

A: No.

Q: Had Ivan creatively reacted to the difference between auto insurance rates in Florida and those in Washington, D.C., where he lived?

A: Yes.

Robbing the Bank

Q: Was the tip-off about the paychecks correct?

A: Yes.

Q: Did the bank have more cash on hand then than usual?

A: Yes.

Q: Did the robbers obtain any cash?

A: No.

He Called the Police

Q: Did he call a co-conspirator on the police force?

A: No.

Q: Before breaking in, had he intended to call the police?

A: No.

Q: Was he arrested?

A: Yes.

Arrested Anyway

Q: Was Rocky wanted for a previous crime?
A: No.

Q: Did Rocky have to change planes?
A: Yes.

Q: When Rocky checked his suitcase, did he expect it to be delivered directly to his final destination?
A: No.

No Ransom Demand

Q: Was the man rational, even though his actions seem inexplicable?
A: Yes.

Q: Is it significant that he was able to bring a firearm past a metal detector?
A: Yes.

Q: Did the man have an accomplice, perhaps someone who was able to sneak a gun into the building for him?
A: No.

Escaping the Kidnappers

Q: Did Brenda get a dial tone, even though the phone had a rotary dial that couldn't be used?
A: Yes.

Q: Did she untie herself, or was she somehow able to break or remove the dial lock?
A: No.

Q: Did she use the telephone?
A: Yes.

People Puzzles

Hearing Them Quickly

Q: Was the father telling the truth?

A: Yes.

Q: Did he intend to keep Dana from hearing the concert?

A: No.

Q: Is it significant that the father was reading the TV listings at the time?

A: Yes.

Motorcycle Madness

Q: Did Amy know those particular motorcyclists?

A: No.

Q: Was she as angry at the motorcyclist trespassers as were Jamie and Peter?

A: Yes.

Q: Did the motorcyclists who managed to escape know Peter or his jeep?

A: No.

A Crying Problem

Q: Did Sandra or her parents-in-law mention any painful subjects or otherwise depart from casual conversation?

A: No.

Q: When her husband's parents said that they were happy for the telephone call, were they telling the truth?

A: Yes.

Q: Did Sandra explain her motive for making the call?

A: No.

She Never Fixed Him Up

Q: Was Mitch genuinely interested in a blind date?
A: Yes.

Q: Did he trust Anna's judgment?
A: Yes.

Q: Was Mitch transferred or reassigned to a kind of work in which a social life would be unconventional or impossible?
A: No.

Happy That She Cursed Him

Q: Was the man a masochist, who generally liked being unpleasantly treated?
A: No.

Q: Did the woman love him?
A: Yes.

Q: Did he believe that her angry words were really directed at him?
A: No.

Evicted

Q: Did the son live in the father's house?
A: Yes.

Q: Was there a physical danger in the house from which the father wanted to protect his son?
A: No.

Q: Did the father own the house and unquestionably have the legal right to have his son live with him (son not a fugitive from justice, etc.)?
A: Yes.

Crazy Cars and Tricky Transport

Driving the Wrong Car

Q: Did each car have a hitch and compatible bumper, allowing either car to tow the other awhile if both worked?
A: Yes.

Q: Was the broken car smashed so it would not tow easily?
A: No.

Q: Was the only problem with the broken car related to its brakes, so the other car could be towed with its brakes partially set?
A: No.

Safe Smash-Up

Q: Was the car controlled by a radio-operated device, as for a movie?
A: No.

Q: Was the car deliberately damaged?
A: No.

Q: Did the car catch fire after its fuel line burst?
A: No.

Contagious Carsickness?

Q: Was there something wrong with the car?
A: No.

Q: When Jan felt sick, were they all breathing fresh air?
A: Yes.

Q: Were they then outside the car?
A: Yes.

What Drained the Battery?

Q: When Walter returned to the car, was anything switched on or the hood open?

A: No.

Q: Had anyone been in the parking lot since Walter parked his car and ran inside?

A: Yes.

Q: Did Walter lock his car?

A: No.

Seasonal Mileage

Q: Does the answer have to do with snow on the ground or snow tires on the car?

A: No.

Q: Does Claude drive along exactly the same roads in summer as in winter, and in the same car?

A: Yes.

Q: Are the windows open in summer, causing much more wind resistance, until closed at the end of a trip?

A: No.

She Arrived On Time

Q: Could Carol have driven from home to the coffee house in two minutes, at less than a hundred miles per hour?

A: No.

Q: Did she use unusual transportation, such as a helicopter?

A: No.

Q: Did Daryl dial her home number correctly and reach her by doing so?

A: Yes.

A Token Wait in a Token Line

Q: Did Smart Stephanie have someone buy her tokens, or go to the subway station at odd, "off-peak" hours?

A: No.

Q: Did she sneak under turnstiles, otherwise evade the fare, or have permission to use the subway without paying (as can some police officers, subway employees, and such)?

A: No.

Q: Did she live in a strictly residential district and work in a strictly business district during ordinary business hours?

A: Yes.

The Late Train

Q: Does the lateness have anything to do with the train's having crossed from one time zone to another?

A: No.

Q: At the time Amanda stepped onto the train, did its crew expect it to become late before she got off it?

A: Yes.

Q: Could this incident, for this reason, happen only at a particular time of year?

A: Yes.

Odd Offices

Stubborn Steve

Q: Did Steve choose paper that was multiple-part, tractor-feed, or otherwise special or unusual?

A: No.

Q: Was the sales clerk completely honest and accurate?

A: Yes.

Q: Was the paper intended for an exotic use that was not reasonably expected by its manufacturer, such as papier-mâché or analysis under a microscope?

A: No.

Making the Grade

Q: Did Nell want a good grade on the course, so that she was planning to have her paper properly written and handed in on or before the deadline?

A: Yes.

Q: Did she have any reason to doubt the receptionist?

A: No.

Q: Is her straight-A average, which suggests good study habits, significant?

A: Yes.

Spaced-Out at the Computer

Q: Can it be done, in general, with only one "replace" command?

A: No.

Q: Can it be done by typing the same "replace" command over and over again?

A: Yes.

Q: Is there another way to solve the problem, one that involves typing three different commands?

A: Yes.

The Fast Elevator Trip

Q: Was the elevator working properly and able to go to the floor where Bill had his appointment?

A: Yes.

Q: Was Bill prevented from getting on, as by a work crew loading a piece of heavy machinery?

A: No.

Q: Did Bill correctly reason that he would get to his appointment faster by not using that elevator?

A: Yes.

The Nonstop Elevator Trip

Q: Were they on a high floor in an office building?

A: Yes.

Q: Did the building have separate groups of elevators to serve separate ranges of floors?

A: Yes.

Q: Could anyone get into a crowded elevator on the ground floor and reasonably expect to get directly to the floor where Bill was, without having the elevator stop at other floors first?

A: No.

Too Precise

Q: Did Jerry and Mary correctly think that vagueness was generally believed important to their business?

A: Yes.

Q: Did they intend to bring profit to their boss?

A: No.

Q: Were they paid for their work?
A: No.

Exceptionally Vague

Q: Did Mary want part of the candidate's political platform to be obscured for any reason?
A: No.

Q: Was it part of a press release or internal memorandum?
A: No.

Q: Did it consist of ten or fewer words?
A: Yes.

The Hostile Voter

Q: Had Charlie decided whom to vote for before receiving the call?
A: No.

Q: Did he think that the volunteer told the truth?
A: Yes.

Q: Did he notice an inconsistency in what the volunteer said that alerted him to a problem?
A: Yes.

A Mystery Fax

Q: Was the call a wrong or misdialed number?
A: No.

Q: If the executive had anticipated the call and connected a fax machine to his telephone line, then would the fax call have resulted in his receiving a fax transmission?
A: No.

Q: Did the executive know who or what originated the fax call?
A: Yes.

Another Mystery Fax

Q: Was the fax a real one, intended to be received and read just like an ordinary fax, with no codes or secret messages involved?

A: Yes.

Q: Did the colleague prefer or insist on a fax in preference to an ordinary phone call, perhaps because of deafness?

A: No.

Q: Did the content of the fax include any tables or other lengthy material that is more easily explained in writing than by speaking?

A: No.

Problems with Personnel

Q: Had the friend seen the advertisement?

A: Yes.

Q: Had the friend followed its instructions and applied for the position?

A: Yes.

Q: Did the personnel department exactly follow the instructions that Raymond had given?

A: Yes.

More Problems with Personnel

Q: Did the colleague and the new person conspire to defraud Raymond's company?

A: No.

Q: Was the colleague thoroughly honest?

A: Yes.

Q: Although the reference-checking turned up no evidence of a problem, was the newly hired person honest?

A: No.

Dismaying Dizziness

Q: Was the dizziness caused by fumes from office machinery or any other source, or related to any toxic substance?

A: No.

Q: If the office had not had the listed changes, then would dizziness result from being in it?

A: No.

Q: Would the dizziness probably be worse after sunset than at midday?

A: Yes.

Asinine Actions

Giving Wayne the Boot

Q: Were the police officers honest and Wayne's neighbor not politically influential?

A: Yes.

Q: Was it the same person who turned on the loud music and threw the boot through Wayne's window?

A: Yes.

Q: Was the neighbor happy when the police arrived?

A: Yes.

Racing the Drawbridge

Q: Was Clarence sensible?

A: Yes.

Q: Did he turn away or stop?

A: No.

Q: If the drawbridge was closed, then would Clarence have approached the bridge?

A: No.

Recycled Salt

Q: Are we talking about ordinary table salt, sodium chloride?
A: Yes.

Q: Is the salt eaten?
A: Yes.

Q: Is the same salt eaten twice?
A: Yes.

Scared of Her Shadow?

Q: Does the sun shine brightly in Florida?
A: Yes.

Q: Is the reason for opening a car window concerned with controlling the temperature in the car?
A: No.

Q: When the sun is shining brightly behind a car, which is not the same as shining in a driver's eyes, is there potential danger because something important cannot be seen?
A: Yes.

Picture the Tourists

Q: Did Sherman want to change places so that he would get better pictures for himself?
A: No.

Q: Was Sherman originally sitting next to a window?
A: Yes.

Q: Was the window open?
A: No.

The Mirror

Q: Is the mirror placed where anyone could look directly into it easily?
A: No.

Q: Is it made from ordinary plate glass?
A: No.

Q: Is it the only mirror that is mounted near the bed?
A: No.

The Empty Wrapper

Q: Was the incident an attempt to cheat the customer, or related to fraud in any context?
A: No.

Q: Did the woman who removed the wrapper from the cart know that the wrapper was empty?
A: Yes.

Q: Was the woman accompanied while she shopped?
A: Yes.

Secret Fuel

Q: Was the gasoline adulterated, the wrong octane rating, or otherwise intended to make the car run poorly?
A: No.

Q: Did the neighbor know of Marvin's activities?
A: No.

Q: Was the car covered by a warranty?
A: Yes.

Forgot to Stop?

Q: One minute before Angus jumped out of the car, did he expect to do so?
A: No.

Q: After he jumped out of the car, did he expect to get into it again?
A: No.

Q: Did more than two minutes pass between when Angus jumped out of the car and when he reached the ground?

A: Yes.

Short-Lived Messages

Q: Does she show them to someone else, perhaps because they are cue cards for a newscaster?

A: No.

Q: Are the messages intermediate steps in mathematical calculations or part of the process of encoding secret data?

A: No.

Q: Are they intermediate steps in an electronic message-handling process that is familiar to the public?

A: Yes.

More Short-Lived Writing

Q: Are computers or any other electronic devices involved?

A: No.

Q: By what she is doing, does she intend to communicate to anyone?

A: No.

Q: Although it is immediately erased, does her output from the writing instrument in turn help erase something else?

A: Yes.

Haphazard Happenings

The Mail Is In!

Q: Had Oscar put the order form into the outgoing mail slot next to the mailboxes the previous day, after that day's mail had been delivered?

A: Yes.

Q: Did the mailboxes have big pods nearby, so that a mail carrier could put a parcel in one of them and the key to that pod in that resident's mailbox?

A: Yes.

Q: Did Oscar pay particular attention to the pods?

A: Yes.

Magazine Subscriptions

Q: Could the need anticipated by those who save them be satisfied by blank paper of similar size and shape?

A: No.

Q: Are they used to cause troublesome paperwork by writing someone else's name on them and then mailing them?

A: No.

Q: Is their reply-paid status very important, more so than for an ordinary postcard?

A: Yes.

Soliciting in Seattle

Q: Do the two friends have similar age and ethnicity, live in similar single-family houses, and live in neighborhoods that, though not close to each other, have virtually identical demographic statistics?

A: Yes.

Q: Is the explanation related to an anti-canvassing ordinance that affects one neighborhood but not the other?

A: No.

Q: Can the difference be traced to the personal convenience of the canvassers?

A: Yes.

It's a Dog's Life

Q: Was the healthy-looking dog less than five years old and truly healthy and uninjured?

A: Yes.

Q: Were both dogs owned by the same owner?

A: Yes.

Q: If not for its serious injuries, would the puppy be expected to live for more than one month?

A: No.

Not from the USA

Q: He was not from the USA, but would he necessarily speak English with a recognizably foreign accent?

A: No.

Q: Was he referring to dry non-USA land, and not an island?

A: Yes.

Q: Could the USA be reached by traveling less than 150 miles north, south, east or west from one point in his home country?

A: Yes.

Dots on the I's

Q: Is a small I with a dot over it commonly seen?

A: No.

Q: If Timmy had written his statement, instead of spoken it, then would the puzzle be easy?

A: Yes.

Q: In his retort, was Timmy talking about the same thing that Jimmy had teased him about earlier?

A: No.

Power Failure

Q: Did Horace sleep away from his house and return to it to find the clocks all stopped?

A: No.

Q: Was he of sound mind and with good vision?

A: Yes.

Q: Did he own an electric clock that had an hour hand and a minute hand?

A: No.

Afraid of the Country

Q: Is Nicolai's background significant?

A: Yes.

Q: Had be been subjected to mistreatment or tortured on a farm in Russia?

A: No.

Q: Would he have enjoyed visiting an actual livestock farm?

A: Yes.

Long-Life Bulbs

Q: Were the bulbs totally ordinary?

A: Yes.

Q: The ordinary incandescent bulbs screwed into ordinary sockets, but could a fluorescent bulb that had a socket base and that fit into the fixtures be used instead?

A: No.

Q: Does the answer have to do with the structure of incandescent bulbs?

A: Yes.

They Had a Ball

Q: Did Ted intend to give Ned practice at running to catch a high ball?

A: No.

Q: Could Ted have aimed the ball directly at Ned if he had wanted to?

A: Yes.

Q: Is their location significant?

A: Yes.

Ballpark Befuddlement

Q: Was the man unhappy with the results of the first two swings?

A: Yes.

Q: Did the final ball go over a fence?

A: No.

Q: Did the man run after the third swing?

A: No.

Crass Creditors and Dull Debtors

Overdue Payment

Q: Did Jim use ordinary first-class mail and *only* first-class mail?

A: Yes.

Q: He reduced the chance of his payment being late because of a postal delay, but did he eliminate it completely?

A: No.

Q: Is it important that Jim sent a payment every month?

A: Yes.

Wrong Order

Q: Did Jim mail both checks, in separate envelopes with ordinary first-class postage, to the same address, from the same town, on the same day?

A: Yes.

Q: Did he mail the lower-numbered check first?

A: Yes.

Q: Did he put both checks into mailboxes?

A: No.

I've Got Your Number

Q: Did Kingfist obtain the telephone number from confederates at the phone company or from Sam's friends?

A: No.

Q: Did he enter the house?

A: No.

Q: Is the fact that Sam's fence was climbable significant?

A: Yes.

Collecting Backwards

Q: Was the check for more than the debt?

A: No.

Q: Was the deposit made in cash?

A: Yes.

Q: Would Kingfist have preferred not to have made the deposit?

A: Yes.

Better Late Than Prompt

Q: If the debtor would have honored the original contract, then would Kingfist have offered the new one?

A: No.

Q: Did Kingfist collect more readily under the new contract than under the old one?

A: Yes.

Q: Did Kingfist collect completely legally?

A: Yes.

The Debtor Paid

Q: Was Kingfist the actual creditor, not a collection agent for someone else?

A: Yes.

Q: Can a creditor use collection methods that a collection agent cannot?

A: Yes.

Q: Did Kingfist receive any of the money that was collected?

A: No.

Daffy Doctoring

She Was in the Hospital

Q: Did Alan and his wife genuinely love each other?
A: Yes.

Q: Nevertheless, was Alan pleased with the news?
A: Yes.

Q: Would his wife have been happy if Alan had tried to visit her when she left the operating room?
A: No.

Appendicitis

Q: Does removing the appendix make appendicitis permanently impossible?
A: Yes.

Q: Did the physician confuse Zeke with someone else or otherwise remember incorrectly?
A: No.

Q: When the physician responded to the call and saw Zeke's wife, did he instantly consider appendicitis even before examining her?
A: Yes.

Crossed Vision

Q: Can you improve your vision by crossing your fingers behind your back?
A: No.

Q: Can everyone benefit from crossing the fingers?
A: No.

Q: Do you need to do something with your crossed fingers?
A: Yes.

Night Blindness Cure

Q: Is medical knowledge necessary to ask the questions or interpret the answers?

A: No.

Q: Are drugs or nutritional supplements needed?

A: No.

Q: Is the setting in which night blindness occurs important?

A: Yes.

A Sweet Problem

Q: Is the sugar swallowed?

A: No.

Q: Can another common substance substitute for the sugar?

A: No.

Q: Under specified conditions, can the sugar be similarly used by people who are not diabetic?

A: Yes.

Miracle Cures

Q: Is the additional explanation known to those to whom it applies?

A: Yes.

Q: When that explanation applies to someone, does it always work?

A: Yes.

Q: After it works, can it ever be identified, even with exhaustive medical tests and scientific scrutiny?

A: No.

Not a Trusted Doctor

Q: Are apparent cures for senility likely to be fraudulent?

A: Yes.

Q: Did Cassandra have any reason to believe the diploma to be counterfeit, borrowed, or stolen?

A: No.

Q: Did the boyfriend know much about Cassandra's past?

A: No.

The Plumber's Pressure

Q: Was the plumber's occupation relevant?

A: Yes.

Q: Was his reasoning correct?

A: Yes.

Q: Was the plumber's earlier ailment a common one?

A: Yes.

Rx Lead Poisoning

Q: Would lead poisoning, the only foreseen consequence of eating lead-based paint, have helped treat the ailment?

A: No.

Q: If not for the fact that his patient was covered by insurance, would there be any reason for the doctor's strange suggestion?

A: No.

Q: Did the doctor intend to treat the lead poisoning?

A: Yes.

Long Walk for the Disabled

Q: Did he park farther to walk more, for the sake of exercise?

A: No.

Q: Did he need to drive another kind of vehicle, perhaps giving up an easily parked bicycle or motorcycle and driving a car instead?

A: No.

Q: Did he own a car and have to alter it because of his injury?
A: Yes.

Eccentric Electronics

Happy with the TV Ad

Q: Had an accomplice damaged the television station, its transmitter, or anything related to it?
A: No.

Q: Did the man hope to sell diagnostic television repair services or TV sets?
A: No.

Q: Would he have been pleased if the test pattern had appeared at a different time or on another channel?
A: No.

Time for Repairs

Q: Did the watch work properly, even though Dilton at first didn't think it did?
A: Yes.

Q: Earlier, had Dilton properly set it to the correct time?
A: Yes.

Q: When Dilton noticed something wrong, was the watch showing an incorrect time from running too fast or slow?
A: No.

Strange Sounds

Q: Are the sounds and pictures out of sync, as when words on a foreign-language film don't match the speaker's lips?
A: No.

Q: Do mistimed sounds—too early or late—give it away?
A: No.

Q: Are some sounds inappropriately absent?
A: Yes.

Watching the Game

Q: Did Elmer use an illegally manufactured descrambler?
A: No.

Q: Did he have an accomplice at a television station or at a satellite company?
A: No.

Q: Did he have a noncompeting accomplice who ran another sports bar?
A: Yes.

Digital Downfall

Q: Do such disks have more background noise than nondigital media or supply the wrong frequency, as can warped vinyl records?
A: No.

Q: Are the enthusiasts concerned only with not replacing their older electronic devices?
A: No.

Q: Can the enthusiasts trace their preference to a scientifically credible explanation?
A: Yes.

The TV Obeyed

Q: Did Jake shout to operate a sound-sensitive switch or, while shouting, manually operate a remote-control device or an ordinary switch?
A: No.

Q: Did Jake see the television screen just before he shouted?
A: Yes.

Q: Videotaped movies usually have their durations printed on their boxes. Is that fact significant?

A: Yes.

The VCR Timers

Q: Is the device's nightly programming ability significant?

A: Yes.

Q: Was the new VCR regularly used to record anything else?

A: No.

Q: Was the hardware store purchase used to alter or disassemble anything?

A: No.

The VCR Remote Control

Q: Did Jenny have or know about a different remote control, perhaps a wall one or one otherwise dog-resistant?

A: No.

Q: Was the television beyond the foot of the bed, well out of reach of someone lying in it?

A: Yes.

Q: Was there something important about the bed?
A: Yes.

No Television Trouble

Q: Is it legal for a television set to be operated so that the driver of a moving motor vehicle can see its screen?
A: No.

Q: Did Stuart know the state trooper, bribe him, or have any special influence?
A: No.

Q: Did Stuart hear the theme music in stereo?
A: Yes.

Inefficiency Pays Off

Q: Does the difference in effectiveness relate to reliability or to relative availability of parts in case of a breakdown?
A: No.

Q: Is an expensive model of the object significantly more likely to be stolen than a cheaper one, making the cheaper one preferable in high-crime areas?
A: No.

Q: Can the elaborate controls be more easily misused than the simple ones?
A: No.

Mad Money

Worth Twenty Dollars

Q: Were some United States currency issues redeemable for gold or silver?
A: Yes.

Q: Could Nick, observing that the Federal Reserve issued the bill, exchange it at a Federal Reserve office?

A: Yes.

Q: Are all United States currency notes legal tender in payment of debts?

A: Yes.

Slow-Witted Customers

Q: Is the policy based on deception or misleading advertising, or otherwise actually or potentially illegal?

A: No.

Q: Are coupons, other marketing devices, or passwords acquired elsewhere required to qualify for special savings?

A: No.

Q: Is this policy, by its nature, impossible to use other than by a fast-food restaurant?

A: Yes.

Banking on the Boycott

Q: Had the fast-food chain borrowed money from the bank?

A: No.

Q: Would the man's idea work only if many people took part?

A: Yes.

Q: Was any law broken?

A: No.

Old Money But Good Money

Q: Were the changes deliberately made simultaneously and with the same intent?

A: No.

Q: Did exactly one of them affect the ideology of why money is considered valuable?

A: Yes.

Q: Was the other considered desirable by some conservatives and ironic by others?

A: Yes.

Secret Business

Q: Did they use scramblers because they suspected that their telephones were tapped?

A: Yes.

Q: In this particular context, would the secure scramblers, which were compatible with each other, have been as useful as the ones that they actually used?

A: No.

Q: Did the men discuss all of their plans on the telephone?

A: No.

Gas-Station Glitch

Q: Was the attendant who announced the five-dollar limit telling the truth?

A: Yes.

Q: Did George, after receiving fuel, receive five dollars in change from the attendant?

A: No.

Q: Was George likely to be one of several angry customers at the gas station?

A: Yes.

Marketing Muddle

Q: Is the car a recent model in the USA?

A: Yes.

Q: Would the name provoke concern if it was displayed, in advertising, only with ordinary letters?

A: No.

Q: Is knowledge of a foreign alphabet important?
A: Yes.

Easy Money

Q: Would Butch keep his word and deliver one complete and working television set for each $30 you paid him?
A: Yes.

Q: Did he obtain the set from the inventory that had cost his employer $45 each?
A: Yes.

Q: Did Butch lose money on the transaction?
A: No.

Too Much Money

Q: Had the investor any reason to suspect shady financing, a conflict of interest, fraud, or anything even remotely dishonest?
A: No.

Q: Would the investor, as a limited partner, give up control of the investment if someone else invested more than he did?
A: No.

Q: Was the money that stopped the investor from investing, money that was already invested in the company or was going to be invested in it later?
A: No.

Goofy Gambling

Lottery Logic

Q: Does it have anything to do with the practice of paying lottery winners in monthly or semi-annual installments?
A: No.

Q: Can lottery tickets be a sensible investment, despite their payouts being biased against their purchasers?
A: Yes.

Q: Are they a good investment for everyone?
A: No.

Youthful Gamble

Q: Is the gambling sometimes managed or controlled by a state government or one of its agencies?
A: Yes.

Q: Are certain young adults not only permitted but also required to gamble?
A: Yes.

Q: Can the gambling be repeated by putting one's winnings at financial risk?
A: No.

Staged Roulette

Q: Could the skit be rewritten so that the roulette bet was concealed from the view of the audience, or removed entirely?
A: No.

Q: Could the roulette wheel be partially hidden?
A: No.

Q: Was gambling a significant problem in that town?
A: Yes.

SOLUTIONS

Welcome, Slasher

A hurricane emergency had been declared, and poorly constructed buildings were at risk of major structural damage. Screens imposed wind resistance which could stress buildings enough to wreck them. Removing screens from screened porches was correctly announced as a safety measure, even if the screens were permanently stapled in place, so the boy had an opportunity to divert his destructive tendencies to a good cause. The policeman knew that the frantic absent homeowners had requested the boy's help with this potential problem.

Evicted

The son, in his late teens, was spoiled and idle. The father correctly inferred that evicting him and forcing him to earn his own way would benefit him, however unpleasant it would be at first. When the son found a job and had worked at it for a while, he understood how his father's action had made his life more respectable and constructive. Therefore, he thanked his father.

What Drained the Battery?

Walter, in a rush, forgot to turn off the headlights. No one else entered the parking lot until lunchtime, when managers customarily went out to eat. One of them turned off Walter's headlights, although by then the battery didn't have enough power to start the engine.

Dismaying Dizziness

The lamp was fluorescent, and the new wallpaper had closely spaced vertical stripes. Fluorescent bulbs do not glow steadily, but flash 120 times per second. When viewing vertical stripes in fluorescent light, the intermittent lighting can make the stripes seem to turn as you turn your head, when they really stay fastened to the wall. This inconsistency is disturbing and is what caused the dizziness. The simplest remedy is to use only daylight. A more practical solution is to replace the fluorescent lamp with an incandescent one.

Smashed Taillights

Bob had been kidnapped and locked in a car trunk. Aware of police department recommendations, he fumbled for the tire wrench and, having loosened it from its storage brackets, broke the taillights and side markers from inside. Then he was able to wave the wrench to passers-by and to call for help.

No Ransom Demand

The man was a cancer patient and was getting weaker and weaker. He had no medical insurance and would soon need hospital care. Confined to a wheelchair, he sat on the gun as he entered the government building. He threatened people in a room next to the district attorney's office so that he would be apprehended as quickly as possible, and he happily went to prison. He knew that, while he was a prisoner, the government would pay his medical expenses and that life as a hospital patient is essentially identical with or without serving a prison sentence.

Contagious Carsickness?

Stan had, as he had planned, stopped the car on a ferry boat. Jan became seasick.

The Nonstop Elevator Trip

The floor was at the top of one range of floors served by one group of elevators. Jill instead used the adjacent group of elevators, going to the lowest floor served by them, which was one floor above her floor. Then, after her nonstop elevator ride, she merely walked down one flight of stairs.

Giving Wayne the Boot

Burglars had cut the neighbor's telephone wire and broken into his house. In self-defense, he barricaded himself into an upstairs room and successfully provoked Wayne to call the police.

The Mail Is In!

Oscar knew the procedure for receiving a package by mail. You take the key from your mailbox, unlock the pod, and take the package from the pod. The key stays in the pod door. Only a mail carrier can remove a key from a pod door. When Oscar saw a pod without a key and remembered that the pod had had a key on the previous day, he knew that the mail carrier had delivered the day's mail.

Afraid of the Country

Nicolai was afraid of silence. While on a farm during World War II, he was exposed to the sounds of livestock. Under normal circumstances, farm animals move around and make noise from time to time. But when scared, they do not. They could hear German bomber airplanes when people could not—and became silent. Silence, to Nicolai, meant that an air raid was imminent and that he would have to hide in the basement. Despite many decades since the war, Nicolai never recovered from his fear.

Not a Trusted Doctor

Cassandra, unknown to her recently met boyfriend, had completed medical school and was a licensed physician. She carefully hid her income-earning ability from men whom she did not know well because she did not want to be exploited. She was as much a doctor as was any other medical school graduate and was telling the truth. She considered the senility treatment worthless, and she said so.

Easy Money

Butch stole the television sets from his employer, making a profit of $30 for each set that he sold.

Supposed to Kill?

A scene was being filmed for a movie. For the protection of actors, it was universally agreed that anyone on the receiving end of a firearm had to load it personally with nonhazardous "blanks." This particular actor had forgotten to load the gun, and the scene had to be refilmed.

Escaping the Kidnappers

A dial rapidly breaks and reconnects the telephone circuit. When you dial a number, you make the dial spin at a controlled rate and temporarily break the circuit that number of times when the dial is released. Without access to the dial, Brenda placed her fingers on the telephone switch-hook (where the handset is placed when the phone is hung up) and removed them rapidly exactly ten times, dialing "0" so as to reach the operator. The operator quickly connected her to the police department.

Seasonal Mileage

Claude uses the air conditioner during summer. Just before the end of a trip, he turns it off so as not to waste fuel. He does not want to pay to keep the car cool while he is not in it. He is sensitive to cold, however; and he keeps the heat on whenever he needs it in winter, including when he is just about to get out of his car.

Too Precise

In a politician's campaign office. They were volunteers for a candidate who believed in straightforward platforms instead of vague speeches.

Racing the Drawbridge

Clarence was navigating a boat, and the drawbridge was opened to let it pass.

Short-Lived Messages

Yolanda has an IBM-compatible computer and an Apple computer and wants to transmit data between them. With only one modem and little technical knowledge, she sends the data to herself through an on-line electronic-mail service with one computer and receives the data with the other computer.

Ballpark Befuddlement

The nine men were practicing golf swings on a driving range.

The Debtor Paid

He went to small claims court, got a judgment, and sold the loan, with its judgment, to a racist extremist group of an ethnic background different from that of the customer. The extremist group was happy to receive the right to harass legally someone of its least-favored race, exceeded the limits of the law in its enthusiasm, and scared the debtor into paying. Laws that restrict collection agents, those who are hired to collect money on behalf of someone else, do not apply to creditors directly. Selling a judgment at a heavy discount can therefore be a prudent business practice, for it bypasses the collection-agent restrictions and may scare other debtors into paying promptly.

Rx Lead Poisoning

Chelation with EDTA is the recommended treatment for lead poisoning, and most insurance companies pay for that treatment. It is also, according to many doctors, a useful treatment for atherosclerosis; but most insurance companies don't pay for it for that diagnosis. The doctor was unwilling to falsify a laboratory test, but craftily noted that the patient could be maneuvered into receiving appropriate treatment that would be insured without the necessity for making any false statements whatever.

Too Much Money

The investor was going to be a limited partner. Someone who invests in a company as a limited partner does not have the right to manage the company, not even partial or voting rights. Such an arrangement is common and completely legal and ethical. Without management authority, the investor wouldn't be concerned about losing control to other investors. What worried him were the personal finances of the people who were going to manage the company. They could have invested all of their money in it, but didn't. If they had a lot of money outside the company, then the investor feared that they expected the company to fail.

Youthful Gamble

College students, despite uniform room charges, are often assigned dormitory rooms of unequal sizes by lottery. Similarly, equal tuition payments do not necessarily result in equal education, because lotteries are used to select which students get access to popular courses that have enrollment quotas.

Burning Down the Building

The landlord set fire to his own building. It was occupied by tenants who paid a low rent that was restricted by law. If they moved out, then he would have vacant apartments that could be offered at a much higher rent than before. Incurring fire damage was a sensible investment, for it would remove the low-rent tenants and permit elegant remodeling into luxury apartments that could fetch a very high rent.

Hearing Them Quickly

The father had noticed the planned live concert and noticed that it was also to be on television. Microphones would be a few feet from the performers and would capture the sound for television transmission. The audience, potentially including Dana, would be farther from the performers than the microphones would be. Sound travels at about 800 feet per second. Television waves and the electric currents that create and respond to them travel over a million times faster than sound. The father correctly figured that the television audience would hear the performance sooner than the live audience, for there would be less delay while sound waves travel the short distance to the microphones and from TV speakers to viewers than while sound waves travel the full distance from performers to the live audience. The difference is only a fraction of a second, but the father was nevertheless telling the truth.

She Arrived On Time

Carol was not at home. She had had her telephone calls diverted to her cellular phone and simply happened to be in the coffee house when Daryl called her.

Exceptionally Vague

It was a label attached to a key to the politician's other campaign office. Keys are best labeled cryptically or so as to mislead, so that they will be easily used legitimately but will be worthless to someone who should not have them. Jerry insisted that the key to the other office, which was at the river, be labeled "River Bank and Trust."

Recycled Salt

Bread recipes customarily call for small amounts of salt. By vigorously kneading bread dough and working up a sweat, one can add previously eaten salt to the dough so that it will be eaten again.

More Short-Lived Writing

Erasing colored chalk from a blackboard. Yolanda is a teacher and sometimes draws diagrams on the blackboard using different colors of chalk. Erasing such diagrams leaves colored smudges on the blackboard. Yolanda discovered that scribbling over the colored smudges with white chalk and then erasing the scribbling helps to remove the colored smudges and, unlike wiping the blackboard with a wet rag, permits immediate re-use of it.

Long-Life Bulbs

Modern incandescent bulbs have a coiled filament that glows as current is passed through it. A coil, however, radiates and absorbs magnetic impulses as the current through it is changed. It thereby not only resists changes in current (the electrical equivalent of inertia), but also shakes slightly as the voltage changes. The voltage changes with alternating current between +166 volts and –166 volts and back again 60 times per second, placing mechanical stress on the filament. Eric merely used direct current, so that the filaments would not be shaken by voltage changes and would last longer for that reason.

She Was in the Hospital

She was a recently hired trauma surgeon and was working in the operating room.

Long Walk for the Disabled

He injured his neck and could no longer turn his head far enough to drive backwards easily. Therefore, he favored parking spaces that he could enter and leave without driving backwards, even if they were a long walk from his destination. To warn away children when he was forced to drive backwards, he installed a warning-tone device on his back bumper and wired it to his backup lights.

Worth Twenty Dollars

Any Federal Reserve bank would have exchanged the $20 bill, but would have insisted that ordinary currency is legal tender in payment of debts and replaced it with another $20 bill. Unless the original bill was damaged by fire or otherwise hard to spend, there is little reason to make such an exchange.

Caught in the Act

In this true story, a neighborhood pickpocket was caught by a woman, the wife of eighteenth-century inventor Peter Cooper, who sewed fish-hooks into her coat pocket. When he caught his hand on the hooks, she told him, "I am going to the police station, and you are coming with me." He cooperated to prevent serious injury to his hand.

Motorcycle Madness

Amy knew that the official penalty for trespassing was merely a small fine. She reasoned that, unable to identify Peter or know whether or not he was armed, the motorcyclists might count themselves lucky to have escaped apparent great danger and would spread the word that that piece of land was unfriendly, thereby encouraging others to stay away.

A Token Wait in a Token Line

Smart Stephanie observed that most commuters bought tokens as they entered the subway from the street. She merely bought tokens as she left the subway, when few other commuters did so.

The Hostile Voter

Charlie heard an aggressive sales pitch about a candidate who supposedly believed in keeping government as unobtrusive as possible. The volunteer was engaged in a meddlesome act, that of telephoning voters at home. Because the candidate approved such intrusive actions, Charlie deduced that the candidate was not going to keep his word about an unobtrusive government and decided not to vote for him.

Scared of Her Shadow?

She drives an old car, with taillight lenses that have not been cleaned from the inside for perhaps ten years. Sunlight shining on taillight lenses can make brake and turn signals nearly impossible to see, particularly with dirty lenses or the dim bulbs in very old cars. Hand signals, under those circumstances, are more easily seen. Florida law permits hand signals for sufficiently small cars, even if the taillights work.

Magazine Subscriptions

Postage for a first-class item with a reply-paid address must be paid by the recipient. City residents may hoard the cards in case of a garbage collectors' strike, perhaps believing that those who contribute to the garbage problem should help solve it at their own expense.

Dots on the I's

A small I has one dot over it. A small I with a dot over it, therefore, actually has two dots, one above the other. Timmy took a pen and put two dots on his forehead, one over each eye.

They Had a Ball

The two men were not alone. Ted saw a teammate behind Ned and feared that if Ned missed the high ball, then the teammate might be hit by it. A throw directly to someone's body was different, for it would at least be deflected if it was missed. Ted aimed his high throw so that if Ned missed the ball, it would not hit anyone.

Appendicitis

Since the earlier surgery, Zeke had remarried.

Happy with the TV Ad

The man was a political candidate running for a local office. Tipped off that his rival had bought a 30-minute infomercial time slot, he bought the minute just before it and broadcast a test pattern, hoping to induce television viewers not to continue watching that particular channel.

The TV Obeyed

Eager to show off his elaborate new equipment, Jake had friends over. Not only did he set up his videocassette player, but also he carefully reviewed the instructions for his television set, which included a timer that would turn it off a specified time later. He carefully set the shutoff timer to outlast the movie by a minute or two and, when the ad came on, saw a warning on the screen that the television would turn itself off in a couple of seconds. He knew that it would be shutting off immediately, so he shouted at the television set just for the fun of it.

Old Money But Good Money

United States currency formerly included silver certificates, which stopped being redeemable for silver in 1968. Since then, there has been no formal precious metal backing to guarantee its value. The year 1968 was also the first year that denominations higher than one dollar suggested the fear of currency devaluations by carrying the words "In God We Trust." Religious zealots favored the wording; some conservative economists took warning.

Slippery Sidney Slipped Up

Sidney was arrested for turning back the odometer and understating the number of miles that he actually drove. While at a distant city, he received two parking tickets from two different officers and didn't pay them. The city charged the fines to the rental-car company, and the company inferred that Sidney had driven the car there. But Sidney had not put enough mileage on the car, according to the odometer, to have been able to do so. The evidence was strong enough to convict him.

A Crying Problem

After she and her husband had a particularly nasty argument, he had stormed out. She suspected that, as he had done previously, he had returned to his parents. Therefore, she called them hoping that they would tell her where he was. When they did not, she became very upset.

The Late Train

During the night, which was the last Saturday in March, the time was advanced from standard time to daylight saving time. The engineer gained fifteen minutes during the night, but the train was still late when Amanda got off it.

A Mystery Fax

Quietly interested in changing jobs, the executive arranged for a cooperative recruiter to try to fax him a blank sheet of paper when trying to reach him. If he could talk, then he announced himself over the fax signal. If not, he called the recruiter later when he could discreetly do so.

Picture the Tourists

Sal's camera focused by measuring the distance to the object in front of it, which would be the window of the bus. Sal's pictures of objects outside the bus would, therefore, be badly out of focus. But autofocus does not work when the distance is very small. Sherman wanted Sal to sit close to the window, so that the camera would ignore it and focus for great distance and would take good pictures.

Forgot to Stop?

The car ran off a bridge and fell into a lake, and Angus jumped out just as the car hit its surface.

Overdue Payment

Jim mailed a check for the late payment. Then he went across town and sent another check for the same amount. If either check was delayed, then the other would probably arrive quickly. He figured that it was unlikely that both checks, if mailed from separate places, would be delayed. And the creditor would have received the next payment early, so that Jim would not have to ask for a refund.

Crossed Vision

If you cross your fingers, then there will be creases at the joints that will allow a small amount of light to pass between your crossed fingers. By looking at objects through the gaps between your fingers, you will expose your eye to only those rays of light that went through one small space. By doing so, you will see a sharply focused image even without wearing eyeglasses. This fact is unimportant except to people who need strong eyeglasses, but who are not wearing them at a particular time.

Time for Repairs

When he first looked at his watch in the morning, it showed the time 10:01. Later that morning, it showed 11:11. During his lunch break, it showed 12:21. The rest of the morning, it did not show the correct time. Dilton was unknowingly wearing his digital watch upside down.

The VCR Timers

Jenny noted that the device was battery-powered and could be programmed to tell the VCR to record Benny's favorite show every night. But if the VCR wasn't plugged in, then it wouldn't record anything. Therefore, Jenny got two 24-hour timers and set them each to be on for 12 hours. She plugged one timer into the wall, the other timer into the first timer, and the VCR into the second timer. Because the first timer delivered power only 12 hours out of 24, the second timer would do a complete cycle in 48 hours. It would deliver power to the VCR during 12 of those 48 hours, and Jenny set the timers so that the 12-hour periods included the time of Benny's show during alternate nights. It was easy to plug the VCR temporarily into an ordinary outlet when playing tapes or for other purposes.

Honest Ivan

Noting the much lower per-day cost of renting a car in Florida than in Washington, Ivan rented the car in Florida. He had it shipped from central Florida to a town in northern Virginia, where he retrieved it. The shipping cost was less than the total savings from renting the car in Florida and returning it to where he got it. By proving that he had sent the car by train, he convinced investigators that the odometer reading was genuine.

She Never Fixed Him Up

Mitch and Anna got married and lived happily ever after.

Stubborn Steve

Steve was going to use the paper in airmail letters to correspondents overseas. To save postage, he wanted paper as light as possible, even if it was expensive and occasionally jammed his printer.

Another Mystery Fax

The executive, aware of how easy it is to communicate with outsiders for undesirable purposes, warned employees that calls would be monitored. A subordinate, aware of the difficulties of monitoring a fax message, bypassed the monitoring by faxing instead of speaking his personal messages.

The Mirror

It is one of two mirrors, both made of special optical-grade glass to prevent eyestrain. The mirror that is not over the headboard is mounted, on a flexible bracket, near it. After adjusting the second mirror, one can lie on one's back and look in it and see the reflection from the first mirror. By looking through two mirrors, one sees an unreversed image. This arrangement is useful for someone with a bad back who wants to lie in bed and watch television, for one need not be propped up but can lie truly flat.

Soliciting in Seattle

In Seattle, one building houses the headquarters of several charity canvassing organizations. They send workers out to collect money, and those workers usually walk from the building when they start canvassing and return to it on foot when they are finished. Only one of the friends' two houses was within easy walking distance of that building.

Wrong Order

He put the lower-number check into a mailbox near his house. Then he drove to the post office and mailed the other check there. Because the second check did not have to wait for mailbox collection, Jim expected it to be delivered sooner than the first check.

Night Blindness Cure

1. Do you get night blindness only when driving your car?
2. When did you last clean and aim your headlights?

The Plumber's Pressure

He had arteriosclerosis, which made his arteries more rigid than those of most people. Measuring blood pressure by compressing an artery and listening is unreliable if the artery is inflexible. The plumber recalled his use of pressure gauges while at work and the ineffectiveness of measuring water pressure in steel pipes by merely pinching them, and he very sensibly wondered if his blood pressure was really high.

Staged Roulette

The police chief had a crooked gambling joint raided and easily obtained a rigged roulette wheel for the show.

Robbing the Bank

The organization was the local police force, and the numerous officers who were standing in line to cash their paychecks easily captured all of the would-be robbers.

Happy That She Cursed Him

She was married to another man, and he suggested that she pretend that he was an obnoxious telephone solicitor if he called while her husband might overhear. His ruse apparently worked, and he was pleased.

Making the Grade

Nell could not hand in a postcard with her term paper because, although the paper was not due for another week, she had already handed it in. She was then free to write other term papers and study for exams in other courses.

Problems with Personnel

Raymond, who was in charge of research, had requested and expected to hire someone with a master's degree. The applicant, who had a doctorate, was rejected by the personnel department because he didn't have a master's degree even though the doctorate was, in Raymond's opinion, preferable.

The Empty Wrapper

She had her two-year-old son with her. When her son got hungry, she got permission from a store manager to buy a sandwich at the delicatessen counter, give it to her son, and pay for it later at the checkout counter with the rest of her merchandise.

It's a Dog's Life

They were at an animal shelter, which had a surplus of unwanted pets and had to kill those that it could not give to willing owners. Fred knew that people were often more willing to adopt a disfigured pet than an intact one. The injured puppy was likely to be taken by a loving family, but the healthy dog had no special claim for compassion and was too old to bond to its owners as strongly as do young puppies. Therefore, Fred expected the older dog to be humanely killed.

I've Got Your Number

Kingfist found the telephone wiring that led into Sam's house and put one pin into each wire. Then he connected a telephone to the pins and dialed a long-distance number that was sure to answer, carefully charging the call on a telephone calling card. A few days later, he called his long-distance carrier and asked about possible misuse of the card and named the number that he had called. He easily learned the number that he had called from.

A Sweet Problem

Diabetic ulcers. According to alternative-medicine practitioners, sugar is a good medicine to apply to skin ulcers, blisters, and other open sores.

Strange Sounds

Some movies in the 1980s had scenes in which someone was typing, but the sounds of the keys were unrelated to the motion of the typist's fingers. Nowadays, scenes of typing conceal the hands to prevent that error. Reverberations remain a clue, as when a person walks from the outdoors into a narrow corridor and the footsteps do not reverberate indoors. Another clue is the absence of a companion sound, as when several people are walking and only one set of footsteps is heard. Or when a horse-drawn cart is shown and horses' hoofs are heard—but the cartwheels themselves are totally silent.

Lottery Logic

Lottery tickets or other risky investments are very sensible when bankruptcy is imminent. Suppose, for example, you have $10,000 in assets and $20,000 in liabilities. If you merely pay your debts to the best of your ability, then you are certain to go broke. But if you buy as many lottery tickets as you can afford, then you have a chance of winning more than what you owe. Then you would be able to pay your debts and have some money left over. Although winning a large amount of money is unlikely, it is possible. That possibility converts certain bankruptcy into a chance to be rich.

Not from the USA

Windsor, Canada, adjacent to Detroit, Michigan, is directly both south and east of parts of Michigan. It is north and west of other USA states.

He Called the Police

Once inside the house, he fell, breaking his leg. Pulling a telephone down from a table, he called an emergency police number for help and, though arrested, received treatment for his leg.

Driving the Wrong Car

The battery on the broken car was dead, and Hermie knew that the electrical system was suspect. He wanted the car checked thoroughly. He jump-started it with the working car, after which it could be driven. The working car had a manual transmission and could be towed without transmission damage. But the jump-started car had an automatic transmission, which is affected by towing. Hermie, therefore, towed the car that had the manual transmission.

Spaced-Out at the Computer

First solution: If you know the maximum number of spaces in a row, take the exponent of the next highest power of 2 and enter the command to replace two spaces with one space that number of times. (Example: seven spaces maximum. Next highest power of two is eight, which is $2 \times 2 \times 2$, so use the command three times.)
Second solution: Choose two characters that are never adjacent in either order (in this example, &%). First command: replace each space with &%. Second command: replace each %& (reverse the order of the characters) with nothing (delete %&). Third command: replace each &% with space.

More Problems with Personnel

The applicant had had a roommate who was transferred overseas and who had impeccable credentials, but he himself was less scrupulous. He applied for work and gave his former roommate's name, background, and references. He wrote to Raymond's colleague and asked about work; they had never met. When the colleague saw that her apparent friend was an impostor, she said so; and Raymond promptly fired him.

Collecting Backwards

Not enough money was in the debtor's account for the check to clear. Kingfist merely found out how much money he needed to deposit for the check to be good, then deposited it and quickly cashed the check. This procedure reduced, although it did not eliminate, the debt.

Miracle Cures

After pretending to have a serious back injury and collecting a large judgment, a malingering patient can go to a well-known source of miracle cures and pronounce himself recovered without leaving any evidence of fraud.

Watching the Game

Satellite signals are generally scrambled. To receive them in usable form, you buy an electronic device (a transponder) and pay royalties to the satellite company, which in turn sets your transponder to unscramble the appropriate signals. Elmer's accomplice ran a sports bar in a distant city and also had a transponder. To obtain unscrambled signals of locally blacked-out games, they merely swapped transponders.

No Television Trouble

A pocket-size television set was on top of the dashboard, and it was off. Stuart was listening to an audiocassette with his favorite show's theme music.

Banking on the Boycott

As the first man suggested, a group agreed to place special orders and overwhelm the help. The second man's strategy involved unusual denominations of money. The first people to place special orders were equipped with fifty- and hundred-dollar bills to force the cash registers to run out of small denominations. By taking a bite out of food before offering to pay for it, the group members would force acceptance of their large bills. The next people in the group got Susan B. Anthony dollars, which are easily confused with quarters, and half dollars and two-dollar bills. These unfamiliar but legal denominations would not fit easily into cash registers and would confuse the cashiers, who would be out of ordinary denominations. Properly done, with angry customers demanding their change, this maneuver would force the chain to generate ill will and lose money.

Marketing Muddle

The Kia is marketed with the crossbar of the A missing: KIΛ. The Λ is the Greek-alphabet equivalent of our letter L, which means that USA customers who know the Greek alphabet may read K-I-L and wonder about the auto's safety.

Arrested Anyway

Rocky took one airplane to an intermediate stop, got out, and got into a second airplane to his final destination. If he had told the airline that he was doing so, then his fare would have been higher. He was trying to save money by noting that the fares for the separate parts of his trip were less than the equivalent fare for the whole trip. Therefore, he could not check the suitcase directly to the final destination, but had to retrieve it and re-check it at the intermediate stop. Rocky did not have a firearm permit for the state in which he made the intermediate stop, but was carrying the gun. He was arrested for that reason.

Safe Smash-Up

No one was in the car. It had been parked on a hill, and the driver who parked it forgot to set the brakes. Since the ignition was not on, there was no spark or other flame source to set fire to the fuel.

The Fast Elevator Trip

When the elevator arrived, other people crowded into it; and Bill critically watched them push buttons for several floors. Bill figured that the elevator would stop at the most floors at which it could stop. Therefore, noting that another elevator was approaching, he decided to get onto it instead; for he would share it with fewer passengers while it made far fewer intermediate stops on the way to his appointment. Avoiding the intermediate stops was worth the wait.

Secret Fuel

Marvin's neighbor had recently bought an extravagant sports car and bragged about it constantly. Hoping to quiet him down, Marvin poured a gallon of fuel into its fuel tank every few nights. After the neighbor began to boast about his new car's outstanding mileage, Marvin knew that his plan would work: merely add fuel quietly, then stop and let the neighbor wonder why the mileage suddenly deteriorated just as the warranty expired.

Power Failure

Power failures occurred often. Horace, therefore, did not bother resetting clocks every time the power was restored. When the power failed during the night, the clocks had not been reset from the previous power failure and looked unchanged in the morning.

Better Late Than Prompt

Kingfist knew that the payments on the original contract were higher than the limit at the small claims court. He restructured the loan so that he could sue in small claims court every time a payment was missed. A small filing fee would induce major inconvenience for the debtor, who would have to repay the filing fee also. By restructuring the loan, Kingfist avoided all collection expenses which he could not recover. The debtor knew that major credit problems would exist from multiple unpaid judgments and scrupulously repaid the debt.

Inefficiency Pays Off

An air conditioner. The models with the most cooling power have stronger motors and cost more than those with less power. But because they cool air substantially, only a small fraction of the air in a room needs to pass through the mechanism to cool a room by a specified amount. Most of the air in the room does not pass through the air conditioner as the room gets cool. What does pass through it is sufficiently cold to cool the entire room. But as temperature goes down, relative humidity goes up. The dissolved moisture in most of the air is not removed, and a too-strong air conditioner makes a room feel not only cool but also damp.

Secret Business

The men were planning a big business deal, and they were pretty sure that their telephones were tapped. They used a simple scrambler that could easily be obtained by an eavesdropper. But before the telephone conversation, they wrote a script for a fake conversation in which they discussed doing the opposite of what they really planned to do. They wanted eavesdroppers to anticipate the wrong plans and lose money, which the two men would gain. A secure scrambler would not have allowed eavesdroppers to hear the staged conversation and would not have helped the two men.

The VCR Remote Control

Except for the nuisance of long cables and a small loss of signal, there is no reason for a videocassette recorder to be close to a television set. Jenny merely moved the VCR to a shelf built into their headboard, where they could both easily reach it while in bed, and connected it to the TV with a long cable.

Digital Downfall

Non-digital media merely record the sound waves as heard. Sound waves consist of fluctuations in air pressure, and a microphone can translate those fluctuations to fluctuations in an electrical signal that is in turn stored on magnetic tape or on a vinyl disk. Digital recording, however, translates the fluctuations to signals that represent the amplitudes and frequencies of the various components of the sound. But those signals don't match the timing of the wave cycles properly, so that the different pure tones that constitute a composite sound may be recorded out of phase and sound different when played back than when first recorded. Partially for that reason, they don't properly record overtones, which are high-frequency sounds that result from two or more lower-frequency sounds in harmony.

Gas-Station Glitch

The man whom George paid was not an employee of the station, but a con artist who got a uniform, asked everyone in line for ten dollars, and left quickly.

Slow-Witted Customers

The menus of the fast-food restaurants offer soft drinks in different-sized cups, labeled "Small," "Medium," and "Large," with correspondingly different prices. Then the restaurants also offer *unlimited free* refills on the same soft drinks!

INDEX

Page key: puzzle, *clues*, **solution**